PETER PULPITPOUNDER, B.D.

PETER
PULPITPOUNDER
B.D.

By

ROBERT E. SEGERHAMMAR

AUGUSTANA PRESS
ROCK ISLAND, ILLINOIS

PETER PULPITPOUNDER, B.D.

Copyright, 1957, by
AUGUSTANA BOOK CONCERN

AUGUSTANA BOOK CONCERN
Printers and Binders
ROCK ISLAND, ILLINOIS
1957

To

CAROL MARIE

whose patience while confined to a sickbed during her sixth year inspired this writing.

Introduction

LIKE TOPSY, this little book is a story that "just grew." It began with chapter one, which was written to entertain the writer's young daughter, Carol Marie, who was confined to complete bed rest following an attack of rheumatic fever. Because this short chapter was enjoyed by his daughter and helped her pass away the time, the author wrote another and another—each intended to be read aloud by Carol's mother or father.

While this story was originally intended for children and to be read aloud as such, it is nevertheless a booklet which might be termed a "child's story for adults"; for adults can see behind the simple, humorous story of a village preacher some reflections of the church's life which are familiar to everyone.

Far from being intended as a ridicule of the minister or the church, these pages are merely written in the realization that a man is to be pitied who cannot lean back and laugh at himself. It is hoped therefore that "brothers in the cloth" will also enjoy this book in the spirit of the children for whom it was written.

Perhaps it should be noted that while the story is written against the background of the small-town church, the writer makes no characterizations of real persons, congregations, or towns. Care has been taken to avoid the use of names and occupations which might coincide with characters in this story

ROBERT SEGERHAMMAR

Contents

Chapter 1

Pulpit Pounding

ONCE IN a happy little village there lived a round man with a straight nose. He had, all at the same time, a pair of long feet and a pair of short fingers—especially one finger which was shorter than all the rest, because this kindly round man was so generous he gave half of his finger away!

Now Peter Pulpitpounder, for that was his name, found it hard to shake an accusing finger at his congregation when he preached, because his finger was simply too short to shake. He might have shaken the same finger on his other hand, but alas—that was his pointing finger, and who ever heard of a preacher who would be so foolish as to shake his pointing finger at his congregation, and then point his shaking finger, when that finger was so short it couldn't point?

There seemed to be no way for poor Pastor Pulpitpounder to stir his little flock until one day, when his voice rose higher and higher, and his straight nose seemed to get straighter and straighter, and he rose taller and taller on his long feet, in his excitement he rolled his little fingers into a great ball and struck the top of his pulpit with such a blow that the ladies jumped from their seats, the babies began to cry, and the sleeping saints were shaken from their slumber. No longer did this fine round man need to wonder how he could persuade his faithful few when he wanted them to believe that his words were true and mighty. He was Pastor Peter Paul Pulpitpounder, and he decided then and there that such a name needed to be lived up to.

Now Pastor Pulpitpounder walked down the aisle after preaching his pulpitpounding sermon and shook hands with the young and the old, the plain and the pretty, the rich and the poor, as they left church to go home for Sunday dinner.

"That was a mighty fine sermon," exclaimed the crooked old grandmother, as she hobbled down the steps with her cane.

"Good sermon, Reverend," said the baker *with a smile,* as he dropped his hat on his humpty-dumpty head.

"Thank you, Pastor," whispered the banker, as he nodded and slipped quietly out of the church.

But one of the ladies, who always sat in the front bench of the church, had a little more to say as she held the pastor's hand. "Now that's the kind of sermon this church needs," she informed her pastor in a voice that sounded as if she wore a clothespin on her nose. "We need someone to wake us up, and that sermon certainly did it today."

It made Pastor Pulpitpounder a little uncomfortable to have his hand held so long by one of his ladies; but if it made him uncomfortable, it also made him proud to think that his pounding was what the people needed. "From now on," decided the Rev. Mr. Peter Paul Pulpitpounder, A.B., B.D., "I shall pound my pulpit every time I would have shaken my shaking finger, if I had a shaking finger to shake."

Before long, everyone in the little village learned that the preacher had found a new talent. Inside the church, everyone listened carefully as the pastor preached and pounded; and outside the church his pounding could be heard by those who always slept too late on Sunday morning to go to church. So far, indeed, did the fame of his pounding spread that people came from far and wide to get a look at this great man and to hear his pounding.

"Good sermon, Reverend," said the baker *with a smile*, as he dropped his hat on his humpty-dumpty head.

13

Chapter 2

Cut-time Preaching

SELDOM HAVE preachers been more foolish than when they have supposed that people think with their heads!

It was a long while before Pastor Pulpitpounder made this great discovery for himself; but when he did, he said to his wife, "Half of my life I spent in school training my head. Half of each week my head works on my sermons. How stupid of me to work so hard with my head when people think with their hearts and not with their heads."

It was a hot day in July, when the village preacher was pushing his lawn mower, that his hat fell off his head. Now this was no simple matter of carelessness, for he dropped his hat because of a startling thought that burst into his funny little head. "It was not in school that I learned to preach," he exclaimed with sparkling eyes. "I learned to preach by beating drum in the band!" For you see, before our friend was a preacher, he was a drummer. He thought, "How I did pound the big bass drum and crash the shining cymbal!" And then he remembered that people always listened best to the band when he pounded hardest on his drum and crashed loudest on his cymbal. "Tomorrow," he promised himself as he picked up his hat, "my pulpit shall be my drum and my ringing voice shall be my cymbal."

The next day was a perfect day for drumming. The sun was bright and the leaves were green, but best of all, it was the Fourth of July. Early in the morning firecrackers were popping and children were shouting.

"What a day," thought Brother Pulpitpounder, "to fire my friends with a drummer's delight! I shall preach as no man ever preached."

The morning service began with a rousing hymn about freedom from the devil and the dictators. The hymns were sung by the congregation with the shouts of Joshua's legions, until the janitor feared the very walls would come tumbling down.

And then came the sermon.

Never before had such preaching been heard in the tiny village. Percussionist Peter introduced his sermon with the clanging of cymbals and the roaring of drums.

15

On through his points of departure he beat, and as he pounded his pulpit drum, the people rose in their fervor until they felt that they were truly "Christian soldiers marching as to war."

Peter continued to depart from his text with the bombast of march time and the after-beat of the snare drum. He called them to their feet with the ringing cymbals of the dogfight and the rolling rumbles of the National Anthem. And when the sermon reached its climax, he defied the unchangeable laws of the band parade and ended his sermon with a stinger—even though he was on the march!

Now Burly Bill, the village plumber, seldom found his way to the Holy House on the quiet Sabbath; but when his saintly wife returned from the church that day wearing the radiance of inspiration on her face, he met her with this query, "And how was the sermon today, my dear?"

"Oh, Bill," she exclaimed, "I have never heard such a sermon in all my life. The preacher carried me away like the wind."

"But what did he say?" Bill inquired.

"Oh," she sighed deeply, "I don't remember what he said, but oh, how he did say it."

And as our pulpit drummer marched home from his church that day, he thought in his funny little head, "Why should I pound so hard with my head, when I can just as well pound with my fist?"

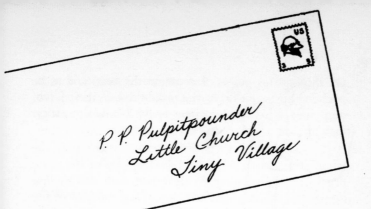

P. P. Pulpitpounder
Little Church
Tiny Village

Chapter 3

What's in a Name

If PULPITPOUNDER was a name to live up to, it was also a name to put up with.

Not only did our reverend friend find it difficult to find room for his name in his Sunday bulletin: others found it difficult to find room for this curious name on their tongues. Indeed, he was more often called by a wrong name than a right one, and his parishioners found it easier to call him "the Preacher" when they talked about him, and "Reverend" when they talked with him, than to call him Pastor Pulpitpounder.

But it was not only outside the parsonage that people had difficulty with so strange a name. It was often said by the whispering villagers that Peter's wife found it harder to decide upon changing to this difficult name than she did in deciding to become a preacher's wife. And his children—well, with a preacher for a father,

17

they found themselves able to say the Lord's Prayer and the Apostles' Creed before they could pronounce their last name.

Confusion also found its way into the Post Office because of this pulpitpounder's name. At times his letters would bear such names as Pulpithammer and Sledgepounder, and once a package bore the label "Rev. P. P. Fistpounder, B.D."

One day to his surprise as Rev. Peter P. Pulpitpounder walked past the town pump in the village square, he noticed a letter in his morning mail addressed: "Rev. P. P. Cigarhammer." He mused in his funny little head, "What if my name were Cigarhammer? Wouldn't my little flock have fun teasing me? I wonder if my little confirmands would call me Rev. Puff-a-Billy or Rev. Holy Smoke during recess? And furthermore, it isn't very dignfied. And who, in my profession, could be dignified with such an undignified name?"

"And also," concluded Peter, "Cigarhammer would be mispronounced as often as Pulpitpounder, and it doesn't have half the punch!" And then he added, "Besides, it's easier to live up to a name like Pulpitpounder than Cigarhammer—especially if you're a preacher."

18

Chapter 4

The Pulpit Outlook

AFTER PETER PULPITPOUNDER developed the fine art of pulpit pounding, his congregation began to look at him more and more when he preached. But if it was nice to have them look *at* him, it was fascinating to see how they looked *to* him. For to Peter, as he stood in the pulpit, the faces of his people were like the falling snow—no two alike. Peter would hardly admit it, but sometimes he forgot what he was saying in his sermon as he thought about the cleverness of God in making so many and such interesting faces and features.

Now, if we children would have the chance to preach a sermon, we would stand in the pulpit and see for ourselves what Peter Pulpitpounder saw Sunday after Sun-

day. We would be surprised to find that our Reverend Mr. Pulpitpounder sees much more from his pulpit than ever we thought he did. How shocked we boys would be to learn how easily he can see us make airplanes of our Sunday bulletins, and how easily his sparkling eyes fall on girls drawing in their hymnals or whispering to playmates. How foolish we would feel to know that our pulpitpounder sees all the little things we do when we think he does not even see us at all!

But it was not only the children that amused Rev. Pulpitpounder when he took his pulpit outlook. Sometimes he thought, "How amusing of the Creator to give the baker a shiny head and the tailor a shiny nose."

And one time Peter almost smiled in his sermon, as he wondered why the Lord gave the head deacon more hair under his nose than above his ears. For the deacon wore a mustache which was so big that from the pulpit it looked as if he had more hair on the front of his head than on the back, and Peter Pulpitpounder wondered which side of his head the deacon combed most when he got up in the morning.

It was no wonder then that Peter forgot how he was going to begin his sermon one Sunday when he happened to notice the women and their glasses. Truly, every color in the spectrum was represented, and Peter doubted that God had shown more originality in His creation than the eyeglass makers had shown in fashioning their glasses—especially the frames.

Peter saw some glasses which reminded him of the tears of repentance, and he saw others that looked like the joy of salvation. One pair appeared like two black

20

tires on display, while another could easily have passed for Joseph's coat of many colors.

But it was not so much *how* people looked as *where* they looked that sometimes disturbed the preacher. There were some who looked at the floor until Peter Pulpitpounder nearly shouted, "Lift up your heads, O ye gates!" And others there were who looked around so much that Peter sometimes wondered if people did not come from the goose instead of the monkey. Of course, in his better moments, Peter knew they did not come from either, because they came from the God Peter Pulpitpounder was preaching about.

Still others in Peter's little assembly looked up into the ceiling when he preached. Now most of them did this, not with their eyes open, but with their mouths open, for sometimes Peter just pounded the air as he preached and the drowsy heads of some nodded heavier and heavier, until they fell fast asleep. But the preacher never worried about his sleeping saints, for he knew he could always arouse them when necessary with a blow of his great round fist.

But one Sunday the little church in the tiny village had a guest preacher, and Peter Pulpitpounder found a place for himself in the balcony. How surprised he was to see that he hardly recognized his people from the back! Heads that looked bald from the front had a little shrubbery in back, and Peter did not know who those people were.

And with all those glaring glasses turned away from him as he sat in the balcony, the room seemed ever so quiet to Peter. When he looked straight down from his

21

balcony perch, he discovered that God used as much humor in designing hair as He did in moulding faces. He saw hair parted in the middle, hair parted on the side, and hair not parted at all. And then, he saw a little boy below him whose hair seemed to start in the middle of his head and spin round and round, like a top.

Suddenly Peter realized, as he looked over these rows of fascinating heads and ears, that he was not listening to the preacher, for he had been thinking how different his congregation looked from the back. "Surely," Peter said to himself, "my people don't do this when I'm preaching. How lucky I am that no one knows what I have been thinking!"

Just then Peter noticed how different the guest preacher looked from the way Peter supposed he looked when he was pounding the pulpit. And as he walked down the balcony steps to take the morning offering he mused, "Do I look as strange to my congregation as they look to me?"

. . . as he looked over these rows of fascinating heads and ears.

Chapter 5

The Preacher's Kids

THE SCHOOL marm with the sternest looking glasses in the congregation would hardly have called the pastor's children "kids," but that is not a bad description; for to Peter Pulpitpounder it seemed that his own boys and girls would eat anything set before them, and the little one in diapers would eat things not set before her.

To be sure, Mrs. Pulpitpounder kept herself from doing things which the parishioners might gossip about, because after she had followed her little one around all day, and had sat up waiting for her big ones half the night, she had little time to get into mischief—especially since the rest of her time was spent on the congregation.

Now few women have greater variety in their work than preachers' wives, because when Mrs. Pulpitpounder grew tired of mopping floors, she could type bulletins, and when it became wearisome to iron white shirts, there was always the black mimeograph to crank.

And seldom is there a woman who is trained in so many businesses of this world, for the preacher's wife learns to run a hotel, operate a restaurant, manage a laundry, conduct a nursery, publish a newspaper, head a music department, and—if time allows so fine a luxury, be a wife to her preacher.

Now like the Lord, Peter Pulpitpounder loved his children most when they were on their knees—not however, because they were praying their prayers, but because they were going to bed. Soon it would be quiet in the house, and he could read a verse in his Bible only once and understand what he had read. But still, it was not only in their sleeping hours that this holy man loved his children. He loved them also when they were awake, although it took more of God's help to love Paul, Jr., when he was sliding down the rainpipe which Peter, Sr., had just repaired; and it was a bit harder to love Peter II when he was shooting paper wads in church made from the children's program sheet. And yet, the pastor loved them all, for they were his—the preacher's kids!

One day Peter Pulpitpounder heard his children called the "p. k.'s." He scratched his bare head with his short finger and wondered what that could mean, until Matthew, age nine and an avid stamp collector, instructed his father, "That stands for preacher's kids." But the longer Peter thought about how ornery his children could be, the more he felt that "p. k." should stand for "papa's kutups."

It was well known to most of the villagers, especially those who lived nearest to the parsonage, that Peter Pulpitpounder's children gave him much help in his sermon preparation. This was not, of course, because they left him to his peace and quiet, for this they seldom managed to do. It was, instead, that his children's trousers proved excellent material on which to practice his sermon delivery, for Peter believed religiously in sparing no rod and spoiling no child. And when the villagers heard frequent pounding resound through the windows of the parsonage, they flipped coins to see whether the parson was practicing his sermon or thrashing his urchins.

One Sunday the Pulpitpounders set off for the annual Sunday school picnic, leaving the back door open, should someone bring them a chicken, or an "ostkaka," or a dozen of eggs. The picnic was exciting as the girls raced with their feet in gunny sacks, and the boys balanced apples on their noses.

Now Peter Pulpitpounder overheard his trustees debating as they watched the contests. His chairman said, "Preacher's kids are always the orneriest kids in the congregation."

The pastor drew closer to his trustees. "Do you know why that is true?" he asked them, smiling. "They learn that from all the other children in the congregation." He laughed, pounding his knee.

They flipped coins to see whether the parson was practicing his sermon or thrashing his urchins.

25

Chapter 6

Daddy's Daughters

"WHAT ARE tummies for, daddy?" This was the question that gurgled from the lips of Helen Margaret, as she squirmed on the living room floor and tried to wiggle from her father, hoping all the while he would catch up with her and tickle her some more. It was a typical question for a two-year-old.

"What are tummies for?" repeated Peter. "Tummies are for tickling on; that's what tummies are for." And once again Peter took the stub finger of his generous hand and tickled his little daughter's round tummy to hear her gleeful giggles.

"Yes," thought Helen's daddy, "tummies are for tickling on." And for a long time he mused upon the won-

26

der of little children, their delightful glee, and their playful spirits. For to little girls, hair is for cutting (with mommy's scissors, but without mommy), and eyes are for sparkling; noses are for blowing, and mouths are for kissing; ears are for pulling (especially daddy's ears), and hands are for getting dirty; to say nothing of the fact that fingers are for sticking in little holes, and feet are for chewing on when they are not being used to run away from mommies or daddies.

But Peter remembered that if little girls' tummies are for tickling on, they are also for filling with bread and cookies and milk and ever so many other delicacies. And he recalled that sometimes it is not so easy to get little girls' tummies filled, because many times when they should be eating their peas, they are smashing them on the table like ants; and when  they are supposed to be drinking their milk, they are finger-painting the highchair with the milk they have just spilled; and when they are not getting their salad and vegetables into their tummies, it is because they are emptying their plates on the tops of their heads.

What parent has not heard the command: "Count for me, daddy." And what is expected? Ask any daddy and he will tell you such a command is an order to assist the princess with her milk.

Now the disposing of milk is a major operation in a home with little girls or boys, for the law of gravity demands that the milk shall be poured down, but the daily question becomes, "Where shall it be poured down?" Shall it be poured down the crack in the table top? Or shall it be poured down sister's half-filled tomato juice glass? In the list of possibilities, the little girl's tummy ranks dangerously low—that is, on her list. And so, if the dark horse is to win in this mad race (and let no one say that it is neither a race, nor mad), assistance must be given by daddy.

To be sure, this assistance must not be given by the hand, for such an insult will bring its protests. Rather, it is assistance rendered with the mouth that is demanded—not that daddy drinks the milk, but that he counts while sister is drinking, or pretending to.

First the counting begins in English; "one, two, three, four, five." At this point, the exercise is stopped and a recess is held. The purpose of this recess is to give the child a breath—should she have drunk some milk.

Then the count continues, but this time in Swedish. "En, två, tre, fyra, fem." Then in German. "Ein, zwei, drei, vier, fünf." Then French is called in to lend its support; then pig Latin; then counting in reverse in English. By this time, the milk is to have been consumed. If it is not, the yardstick is quietly placed beside the table, and a gentle reminder is given that words must sometimes be strengthened by action.

Once Peter thought that with clever tricks he could get his little girls to drink their milk. But after much experience, he decided that mixtures, straws, pouring into smaller glasses and all such devices for milk drinking are as deceiving as the devil himself; for they seem to work for a season, but later they cause nothing but grief and pain. As the Good Book says—"Flee from all such."

And so it is with daddy's daughters. But while little girls are for giggling and gurgling, and laughing and crying, and teasing and trying, and shouting and singing, they are also for sleeping like little cherubs in the moonlight with hallowed hair and angelic countenance, for standing by silently in the nursery at night, and for praying about to the heavenly Father who watches over them with tender care. Who can list all the things little girls are for? For like the dear Lord who made them, little girls are mostly just for loving.

Chapter 7

The Preacher Goes Fishing

"IT DOES my heart good to see you working for a change," said farmer Johnson, as he stood with his hands folded under the bib of his clean "town overalls," and watched Peter Pulpitpounder trim the hedge.

Peter wanted to rise on his long feet and straighten his straight nose, and raise his loud voice as he did in his pulpit, and tell this good farmer that preachers do not work only with their hands. He would have said it, but he was afraid he might pound the hedge as he answered and tumble from his perch on the ladder. Instead he quietly told his head usher, "No, John, I'm afraid you're wrong this time. I'm not working now; I'm relaxing, while I set my real work aside for a bit." He wanted to tell John there are other kinds of work besides the kind people do with their hands.

But one Sunday evening, when Peter had returned

30

to the parsonage after his vesper service, he announced to his family, "Everyone gets a day off on Sunday but the preacher."

Carol Marie, his sweet six-year-old who was recovering from rheumatic fever, offered her bit of help. "But daddy," she explained, "you don't have to work the rest of the week."

But one day when Carol's mommy was reading Bible stories to her, she explained how preachers work just as hard all through the week as they do on Sundays—sometimes harder. "The only difference," said her mother, "is that the people don't see your daddy work on weekdays."

This set Mrs. Pulpitpounder to thinking. "Why shouldn't daddy have a day off like every other man?" She thought, and she thought, and then she thought again. And when she thought still another thought, her face began to beam like the rising sun. She had been wondering what Peter could do on his day off (if he took one), and now she had the golden answer. "He can go fishing," she told the rye bread which she was taking from the oven.

At first Peter just knew he could not take the time to go fishing. But women have their way with men, and finally Peter was a fisherman, but so far, of course, only in imagination.

At last the day came when the pulpitpounder had bought his fishing tackle and laid his books on the shelf. The boots were in the car. The flies, the leader, the reel were carefully checked. The cookie jar was generously raided. Even the worms which Peter dug the night before were not forgotten.

31

But then, just before Peter kissed his family goodbye at the car, Luke, his oldest son who was a medical student, called from the house, "Dad, a couple of people want to see you."

The embarrassed look on the faces of these two strangers, the hesitancy in their voices, and the little certificate in their hands gave it away immediately to Peter. While the couple waited, Peter changed from his fishing togs to his pounding togs, and when bedtime came, he was still in them.

But although this was a common thing for Peter when he tried to go fishing, it was not the way it always happened. And before he knew it, Peter found that he loved to cast his line as much as he loved to pound his pulpit. And one bright day on the shady side of the stream, he told his pastor-friend, who was fishing by his side, "I love to be a 'fisher of men.' But I must live up to my first name also, because I love to be a 'fisher of fish.' "

Chapter 8

The War Department

PEACE AND HARMONY usually prevailed in this little church in the tiny village. Hardly a Sunday passed but the church was filled to hear the preacher wind the forge and pound the anvil. Hardly a Sunday came that the ushers failed to appear (at least by the time of the opening hymn), and hardly a Sunday went by that the janitor did not remember his regular ritual of striking a match on the seat of his pants to light the altar candles after the congregation was seated—a practice Peter tried to change. But changes are not easily made in those churches which are made up of people.

But alas—and who would have thought so—the sourest harmony was found where blending should have been the sweetest. You guessed it—in the choir! How saintly they did look in their lovely robes on Sunday morning, and how sinfully they could act in their shirt

33

sleeves on Thursday night. For while love covereth a multitude of sins, black robes and white collars do not, and neither does it help to add a white surplice and a purple stole.

Little need then should there be to say that Peter Pulpitpounder looked upon the disharmony of his choir and said something quietly about the "war department of the church." For Peter could forgive the dissonance of the chorus, but it took patience to accept with thanksgiving the disharmony of the choristers.

Now in this little church, the pulpitpounder was also the choirmaster. For who could better help these singers offer their sacrifice of praise to the Lord and display the marvels of the voice to the congregation than Peter Pulpitpounder, who had learned so well how to beat the air—to say nothing of the fine tenor voice of this straight-nosed man, especially when he rose high on his long toes?

One Saturday night as Peter Pulpitpounder lay in bed, he tossed and tossed. He was not worrying about his sermon, tho' it needed brushing. He was not fretting over his Bible study for the Young Married Couples' Class—a class of men and women in their late fifties. Not even was he disturbed about the board meeting he was having with his trustees after church when they were to decide how they should spend the thousand dollars Aunt Josephine had donated as a memorial to Uncle Joseph. Instead, Peter was tearing his covers apart trying to see how he might make a peace pact with his choir, for they were in one of their cold wars because Tillie, the tremulous soprano, was carrying the solo in the anthem, and Vera, the village vibrato, thought it was her turn to sing the descant.

Peter prayed, Peter tossed, and Peter scratched his long nose. And then suddenly he turned on his back, pulled the covers up with his short fingers, pointed his long feet heavenward and sighed, "Well, anyway, they do sing nicely; and who ever heard of the battle of the saints in the good fight of the faith without a war department?"

(A Meditation in a Weed Patch)

Chapter 9

The Ladies' Aid

"MEETINGS, MEETINGS everywhere," Peter groaned.

"And plenty of coffee to drink," was his wife's helpful response.

But Peter Pulpitpounder was in no mood to be funny. Had he not gone to thirteen organizations this month? And who likes to attend committee meetings night after night until he gets that committee-complex? "Frankly," said Peter, "it's bewildering, not to mention exhausting. I wonder what it's all about?"

One day, while the Right Rev. P. P. Pulpitpounder, AB., B.D., was cutting his weeds in his massive back yard which his little congregation thought was just the thing to give the preacher some exercise (because it must be ever so tiresome to sit around so much)—while the weeds were flying and Peter's brow was dripping, this reducing round man looked back at the acre of lawn he had just cut and forward to the two acres which was to be his challenge of the morrow, and exclaimed, "Heavens!"

Now this was not a very nice word for a preacher to say. But it was nevertheless the best word that Peter Pulpitpounder could find in his Biblical Dictionary that was at once strong enough to be good for shouting and mild enough to get by with, should anyone from his congregation overhear him. And so the dignified "man with the scythe" looked across the fields of grass and whispered, "Heavens."

"There is much in this job of mowing grass that reminds me of organizations and committee meetings," Peter groaned. "I no sooner get half done than it's time to start over again."

"Yes," offered his wife, who was sitting in the shade changing diapers, pitting cherries, shelling peas, and reading a book, "and furthermore, there are many kinds of weeds out there. Some come back a second and third time, and others don't ever come back, once they have been nipped in the bud."

"Let us remember that people are people," replied the preacher, as he adjusted the suspenders of his bulging "levis." "We must not forget that a lawn is also beautiful and useful, and sticks to its job—just like our good ladies."

"And anyway," Peter continued, as he laid down his scythe and began to trim around the trees (for rest), "we have the finest ladies in our Aid that ever were; and besides, that's one place where I never need to pound my fist."

Chapter 10

The Preacher's Inspiration

"BUT PASTOR," said Mrs. Peterson smilingly, as she set her coffee cup beside her cake and salad, and sandwich and pickle, olive, cookie, and peach sauce, which was the light lunch served at Aid that afternoon, "where do you get your inspiration to preach such inspiring sermons?"

Peter Pulpitpounder looked at the floor in embarrassment. Indeed, he almost spilled his coffee as he squirmed and turned and groped for a reply that would express both his modesty and his delight in being told his preaching brought inspiration to his people. He mumbled something in broken sentences about prayer, and Bible study, and the help of the Lord; but he was too surprised by this gracious remark to think and speak with the ease that he did in his pulpit.

But later, after our good friend and pastor had thanked his hostesses for their tasty feast, and had talked with all the ladies and their committees about their problems and their projects, Peter slipped quietly into his study to think more carefully about the source of his inspiration.

"Can a pastor preach about love unless he lives in the spirit of love himself?" he asked as he closed the door. "And where does he find his love if not in his home?"

he thought, pacing the floor. For whatever Peter's home was of struggle and worry, or balky budgets and busy rushing, or even of bitter illness that put one sick child in each of the seven bedrooms of the big parsonage, or put all seven sick children in one bedroom of the little parsonage, the Pulpitpounder home was above all else a haven of tender love and sweet affection. And as Peter thought longer and longer on this subject, he became more and more certain that his inspiration came from the wife he loved, and who loved him, and the loving Christian home they had together. And so it was that Peter Paul's mind went sailing about in a happy and pleasant excursion. He recalled how he and his wife had never had a major battle nor a ten-round quarrel in all the many years of their marriage. To be sure, there were differences of opinion from time to time, but never did they fail to work out these differences by talking things over in kindness and understanding and forgiveness.

And then as the pastor remembered the many couples who came to him with family problems, he thought of all the ugly habits that creep into some homes—like jealousy, and criticism, and cutting remarks, and useless suspicions, and mean tricks, and little lies to cover up. And as he thought of all these little termites that eat away some homes, he folded his stubby fingers, and thanked the loving Lord that these little enemies had never stolen into his home to tear it apart and leave it in crumbled ruins.

But then, as Pastor Pulpitpounder thought of his wonderful family and its joyous inspiration, he wondered why his home had been spared by this strange matrimonial angel of death, when so many other homes are entered and destroyed. And as he pondered and prayed, he noticed that the spirit of his home was much like the spirit of Jesus. For it was Jesus who lived in the spirit of love and kindness, mildness and meekness, forgiveness and helpfulness, and above all else, the willingness to overlook little things and go more than half way in treating everyone like a dearest friend.

So Peter saw that, by his Father's help, the spirit of his home was like the spirit of Jesus—at least as far as weak and stumbling people can make it so.

And he said to the new pen and blotter set on his walnut desk, "What an inspiration to have a home where each one lives in the spirit of Jesus, and to have a wife who is not only beautiful, but also loving and sweet and understanding—like Jesus! Surely this is the preacher's inspiration!"

41

Chapter 11

Weeping Over Jerusalem

ALTHOUGH PETER PULPITPOUNDER was skilled in pounding his fist, he was not one to lose his temper. Indeed, Peter was usually a very, very happy man.

But there were times.

Not that Peter lost his temper during those times. Instead, he would become very, very sad. His sadness usually came when Peter sat alone. Sometimes it was when he was alone by the river bank, and sometimes it was when he was alone in his study with its walls lined with books. Sometimes it was when he sat alone in his own back yard at twilight, for there is that about being alone with quiet thoughts in the dusk of evening which brings a strange, wholesome sadness to the heart.

Now Peter was not always sad when alone, but when alone, he was sometimes sad. He would think about people. He wondered why they would spin around so fast and yet spin so little.

He wondered why they made themselves their own worst enemies by being jealous, or suspicious, or fearful.

He wondered why folks spent so much of their talking-time hurting their neighbors and so little of their praying-time helping them.

It made Peter sad to see how people find it hard to give anything away for the sake of Jesus, when Jesus gladly gave everything away for them. He was so sorry that his villagers slid down in their chairs when someone was to be appointed a job at the church, when they knew in their hearts that Jesus wanted them to rise up from their benches and serve Him willingly.

Sometimes Peter felt more like pounding "britches" than drying eyes—as when his Board wanted to spend dollars on the village church at home, and dimes on the village church in Africa; or when some of his members used the same mouth to swear with in Jesus' name in the day time as they used to pray with in Jesus' name at night. For Peter pounded his pulpit in preaching the cross to his villagers, and sometimes he felt that the nails were pounded through his hands, too.

One day, when the bullheads were not biting, Peter Pulpitpounder let his thoughts wander off into that little room in his heart called "Sadness." He thought these thoughts of sadness, as the wind made the tall grass look like waves in a green sea.

And then a strange thing came to pass. It seemed a whisper was in the wind, as it bent the shady grass, and it said, "I know your sadness, Peter. It is my sadness too. It is the sadness of a heart that bleeds because the world will not listen—the sadness of a soul that cries out, like a hen whose chicks will not be gathered under her wings."

Peter scratched his sad, smooth head. Then he confided to the squirming worms in the rusty can, "I guess it is better to be glad for those who 'will' than to weep about those who 'won't.' "

"Besides," thought Peter, "the rest is up to Him whose voice is in the rustling wind."

Chapter 12

D. D.

WHAT IS a rally without a pounding fist?

At a rousing rally, pounding fists are to the pulpit what streamers are to the rafters. And who would make a better rally speaker than the Rev. Peter Pulpitpounder? His pounding was improving, and many a sermon was "full of sound and fury."

Little wonder, then, that the village saw less and less of this fine round man, for he was called here and there, up and down, and all around to give a rally that needed punch. The more he traveled, the rounder he got. And the bigger he got, the greater people thought he surely must be. The harder he pounded, the larger the print in the morning paper which told about his rallies. Soon the village preacher was called to college graduations, and the students just knew they were hearing the greatest speaker in their lives as they saw this round, round man and heard his pounding, driving fist.

But not all was "sound and fury." The mighty preacher of the tiny village was a man with a heart as big as his waist was round, and his thoughts were as deep as his feet were long. And although his fingers were little and one was too short for shaking, his hands were generous, and he gave freely to all who came to his door, both of food and money, and especially of his time.

Such a man would be called to bigger things. Said one city preacher as he visited with his friends at a convention, "Let us elect a village preacher for our president. Village preachers have little to do, and such a job would give one village preacher a chance to keep busy, and also relieve the busy city preachers who have big churches."

Perhaps it was for this reason, perhaps it was because Peter Pulpitpounder was known everywhere for his pounding, and perhaps it was even because he was so good and kind—for whatever reason it might have been, the Rev. Peter Paul Pulpitpounder, A.B., B.D., was elected their president, and everyone in the room voted for him.

Peter was at once humble and happy. He knew that he had a great task, but he was happy to do what he could; and he was sure that a pounding fist would be first-rate equipment for a president.

And then it happened. Peter had served well as a president. He had traveled far to pound pulpits all over the land, and now he was invited to be called "Doctor" and not just "Reverend" as most of his brother preachers were called. To the

college campus Peter went; and Mrs. Pulpitpounder ruffled her little handkerchief, as she saw the professor shake Peter's hand and offer him a certificate. For Peter was a pastor who had done so much for so many people, he deserved to be honored in this way, because here was a man who possessed a dramatic dignity—a dignity that was not donated.

And what did the certificate mean? Oh, that might not be good to say; for some think it means this, and others, that; but one thing is sure: it meant that from now on Peter Pulpitpounder was a "Doctor of Divinity," and he could add two more letters to his name. Now he was Dr. Peter Paul Pulpitpounder, A.B., B.D., D.D.; but when Peter returned to his humble village, his parishioners still just called him "Reverend."

Chapter 13

Door Pounding

NOT OFTEN is the urge to be a boy again satisfied so well for preachers as when they go calling. Not that pounding sidewalks and stormdoors is in itself a fountain of youth, although such exercise has its merits. For it is not in going to or from a home that the preacher is made to feel like a boy again. Rather, it is the conversation which takes place once the caller is inside the door which sometimes gives him this boyish feeling.

Some of Peter's calls were like the last visit he paid Mrs. Johnson. He drove from the parsonage in his faithful car, leaving behind many serious and important matters from sermon preparation to church business. He had just arranged his meeting with the Board, and although his report to the hospital administration was not yet complete, and even though a man and his wife were coming that afternoon to counsel with him about a serious family problem, Peter felt he had just enough time to make this one call on Mrs. Johnson.

The pastor rapped on the door.

"Well," exclaimed Mrs. Johnson in the voice of impatience as she threw open the door, and sunk her hands into her sides, "imagine such a surprise! I wondered if you were ever going to call at this house again. It has been no less than six months since we've seen you here."

It was then that Peter felt like a boy again—a school boy being scolded for coming tardy to school, and told that he could stay in for recess.

And then there were evening calls to make. Peter did not like to be a "ladies' pastor," so he frequently left the home fires at night to call in those homes where the man of the house is always away at work in the day time. Some of these calls reminded Peter of his younger days, too.

Now such calls reduced the Pulpitpounder's self-esteem not by what those people said, but by what they did not say. The rock of offense was often television.

The usual knock at the door brought a person with an unusual expression on his face. It said two things. The first expression said, "Oh, we're so happy to see you, pastor. We love to have our pastor call." But at the same time and on the same face another expression could not be hidden. This one said, "What a shame you came tonight. This is my night to watch wrestling."

And once again Peter felt like a little boy—a little boy who came downstairs while the party was going on, and was handily hustled back to bed.

There was a third time when Peter's calls made him

feel like a little boy. This time it was when he called on people who never go to church. Now not every family that stays away from church is like this, though many are. The pounding knuckles of the clergyman are heard inside. The door is opened. An expressionless face and a monotonous voice say, "Well?" Peter explains that he is the pastor of a church and would like to visit these new friends. The door is shut, and amid the rustle of the hinges it seems to Peter that he hears something like, "Not interested." And again Peter feels like a boy—a little boy peddling horseradish from door to door.

But it was not always so. Peter was often made to feel like a boy for reasons which are ever so pleasant to think about. For many a time our reverend messenger pounded doors that were opened wide and was met by people with open hearts. And such things made him feel like a boy, too—because his heart, which was sometimes heavy, was often made light by a good visit with an appreciative soul; and many indeed were the times that Peter felt that his most useful work was done when he called on his people. And when these things happened, Peter was inspired and renewed in his spirit, fresh and happy—just like a boy!

Pounding doors, like pounding pulpits, has its ups and downs. But Peter Pulpitpounder for one decided there were more ups than downs in door-pounding— as when he called on the sick, the sorrowing, the troubled, or even when he called on the plain people on plain days, when they were just plain glad to see him and he was just plain glad to be with them, to share with them his faith and his Lord and his Bible, and listen to their tales of weal or woe.

And one day, when Peter parked his car in the garage, and kissed his sweet ones in the kitchen, as they were setting the table for supper, he said, "In my work there seems to be all kinds of pounding to do—pounding pulpits, pounding typewriters, pounding doors, pounding sidewalks, pounding things into people's heads—pounding, pounding, pounding!"

"Yes," returned Helen Margaret, his radiant preschooler, as her eyes flashed toward her daddy's hands, "we must keep pounding away all the time. And it's all very nice—except when you pound my britches."

Chapter 14

Peter's Pounding Heart

THERE WERE times when Peter did not pound. Or might we better say, the pounding was sometimes of his heart, and not his hand. For though this kindly man could make others hear the pounding of his hand, Peter could also hear the pounding of others upon his heart—pounding of sorrow, and pounding of joy, pounding of pain, and pounding of need.

Now Peter's heart was a big heart, and the pounding of his fist was only the echo of a heart that pounded with faith, and hope, and a kind of charity that had, mingled in its silver cup, the sweetness of sympathy and tenderness and heaven's understanding.

It was his heart that pounded when Pastor Pulpit-pounder visited the oldest grandmother in his parish, and read to her about the Good Shepherd. It was his heart that pounded when the poorest man with the largest family in the village talked late into the night with Peter, laying his problems on someone he knew would care. It was his heart that pounded when Peter baptized the babies and taught the children about the Father who provides for birds and flowers, and even for us—His children. And it was his heart that pounded when Peter sat with his disciples, big and small, around the breakfast table and led them in morning devotions.

Now, Peter was a busy man with studying to do, and

letters to write, sermons to prepare, and records to keep, visits to make, and meetings to attend, phone calls to answer by the dozen, and problems to solve by the hundred. But if Peter was a busy man, he was also a willing man; and never, never was he too busy to wipe some little tear or pat some proud shoulder. For above all else, Peter Pulpitpounder was a pastor; and while pastors come in different weights and sizes, they always come with pounding hearts.

Perhaps the heart of our dear pulpitpounder beat the most unevenly whenever he was invited to move to another congregation. Then it was that he pounded the doors of heaven to ask what his heavenly Father wanted him to do.

One day, after turning away many other invitations to move, the Rev. P. P. Pulpitpounder found himself nervously sitting at a party in his little village church. It was called a farewell party, and Peter's heart pounded and pounded. But Peter's was not the only heart that pounded that day. The butcher, the farmer, the elevator man, the barber—all had hearts that pounded higher and higher, as their memories went back farther and farther. "Central" had a heart that pounded as she remembered the many times her pastor had called her to ask if such and such a one were still in the hospital, or the many times she had informed him, when he rang, that this family or that family had gone out of town for the day, and could not be reached by phone. Even the little man who talked behind the pastor's back when Peter preached about money—even this man's heart pounded.

Finally Peter arose to talk to his little flock for the

last time. He felt the familiar touch of the pulpit rail upon his hand, and as his heart pounded, his fingers began to roll into a little ball. He looked at his faithful many (for big crowds are always on hand at receptions and farewells), and with the pounding of his fist, he cried, "I cannot say farewell! But as I leave, I want to say, 'Remember Jesus Christ.'"

And then after a heart-pounding pause, he continued, "It was for Him that I pounded on your heart-door. It was for you that His hands and feet were pounded to the cross." And then, as a warm tear fell lightly where his pounding hand had so often fallen heavily, Peter Pulpitpounder said quietly, "Your life must be your pulpit. Pound it with heart and hand . . . for Jesus . . . 'til He comes."

And when the Rev. Peter Paul Pulpitpounder, A.B., B.D., D.D., said this, he thought in his funny little head, as he looked at his funny little congregation for the last time, "I wonder if I will pound my pulpit-drum in heaven?"

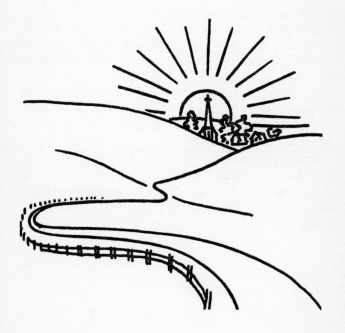